THE LORD
SHEPHERD

JAN GODFREY
AND HONOR AYRES

'A long time ago, David was a
shepherd boy, looking after his sheep.
He wrote many songs. One of them is
called Psalm 23. It's about how much
God loved and cared for him.

God loves and cares for people now in just the same way. The Psalm is just as true today as it was for David – and not just for shepherd boys but for you and me and everyone else!

'The Lord is my shepherd,' sang David,
the shepherd boy.

David loved God very much indeed.
He often thought about God and sang songs to him,
as he wandered over the hills and looked after his sheep.
They knew his voice and he knew their different 'baas'
and 'maas', their bleats and cries.

'The Lord is my shepherd and I have everything I need,' sang David, the shepherd boy.

David knew that God gave him good things - food to eat, shelter from the cold, and clothes to wear.

'The Lord is my shepherd and I have everything I need. He lets me rest in cool, green fields,' sang David, the shepherd boy, as he rested with his sheep in the shade, on a hot and sunny day.

'The Lord is my shepherd
and I have everything I need.

He lets me rest in cool, green fields and he leads me to pools
of fresh water to drink and splash in,' sang David,
the shepherd boy, rested and refreshed
with his flock of sheep.

'The Lord is my shepherd and I have everything I need.
He lets me rest in cool, green fields
and he leads me to pools of fresh water
to drink and splash in and
to give me strength.

'And he shows me the right way to live,'
sang David, the shepherd boy, who led and
guided his sheep along the right paths, to
keep them safe.

'The Lord is my shepherd and I have everything I need.
He lets me rest in cool, green fields and he leads me to pools
of fresh water to drink and splash in and to give me strength.

'He shows me the right way to live and he's promised to be
with me all the time, even in the dark, when I might be afraid,'
sang David, the shepherd boy, as dusk turned into night-time,
and the sky was lit only by the stars.

David used his strong shepherd's crook
to help him climb over stones and rocks,
to find straying sheep or lost lambs,
and to keep dangerous animals away.

David knew that God's love was like
a shepherd's crook, strong and firm,
keeping him safe.

Then David the shepherd boy sang to God:
'Everyone, even people who don't love you,
will watch as you get a special meal ready for me –
a really big party, a feast, a celebration! I'll be your
special guest at the table, because you're my good
shepherd.

'And everyone who loves you will be there,
because each one is very,
very special to you.'

'You'll fill up a cup for me, right to the very top,'
sang David the shepherd boy to God,
as he danced for joy amongst his flock of sheep.

The sheep danced for joy too. They jumped and they jiggled and they wriggled their tails. They ran and hopped and skipped and then they rested and munched the sweet, juicy grass.

'You'll fill the cup to the very top so that it overflows
and spills over with praise and happiness and love
and life for everyone,' sang David, the shepherd boy,
to God.

'I will know your goodness and love today and tomorrow and the next day and ALWAYS!'

David watched the sheep running about in the fields together. Sometimes they ran in front of David, and sometimes behind him.

'You'll always be with me and stay with me,' sang
David, the shepherd boy to God, 'all my life, close
beside you, for ever and ever, because...

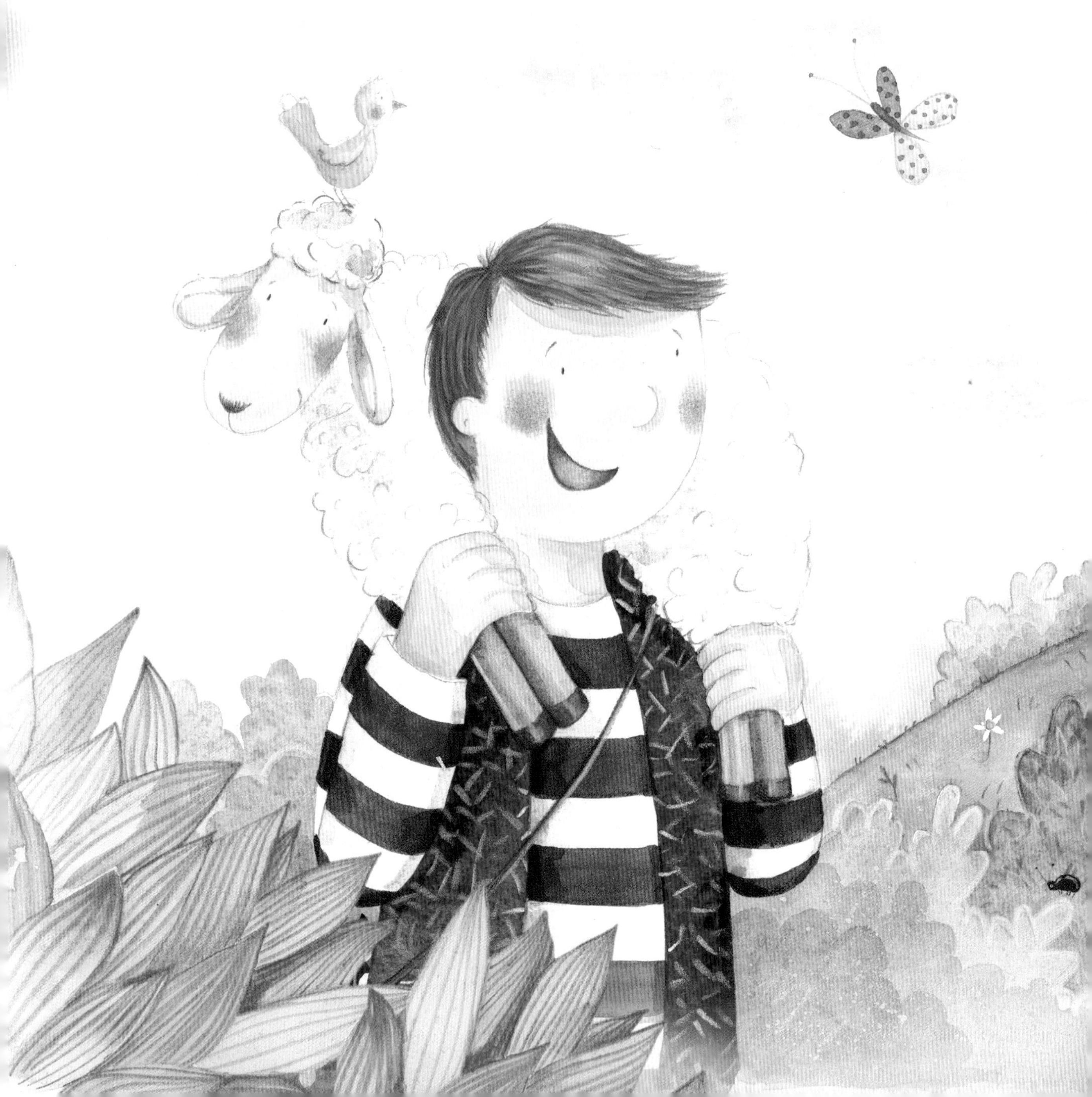

'... you are MY good shepherd.'

Psalm 23

The LORD is my shepherd,
I shall not be in want.
He makes me lie down in green pastures,
he leads me beside quiet waters,
he restores my soul.
He guides me in paths of righteousness for his name's sake.
Even though I walk through the valley of the shadow of death,
I will fear no evil, for you are with me;
your rod and your staff, they comfort me.
You prepare a table before me in the presence of my enemies.
You anoint my head with oil; my cup overflows.
Surely goodness and love will follow me all the days of my life,
and I will dwell in the house of the LORD for ever.

NIV